Depression

 caring for yourself and others

PASTORAL · OUTREACH · SERIES ·

Depression

 caring for yourself and others

Dr Adrian Treloar

redemptorist
p u b l i c a t i o n s

Published by Redemptorist Publications
Alphonsus House, Chawton, Hampshire, GU34 3HQ, UK
Tel: +44 (0)1420 88222, Fax. +44 (0)1420 88805
Email: rp@rpbooks.co.uk, www.rpbooks.co.uk

A registered charity limited by guarantee
Registered in England 3261721

Copyright © Redemptorist Publications 2017
First published November 2017

Series Editor: Sister Janet Fearns
Edited by Kathy Dyke
Designed by Eliana Thompson

ISBN 978-0-85231-503-3

Printed by Lithgo Press Ltd.,
Leicester, LE8 6NU

Acknowledgements

*I am hugely grateful to my long-suffering family for supporting me as I write
this book. I am also grateful to all those people and patients who have taught
me so much as we journeyed together through their illnesses.*

Introduction

Depression can be a difficult and unpleasant illness. Seeing people suffering with depression can be very hard, especially for family members. Giving care and support can also be very challenging for friends, family and many others, including church members. But to support people while they recover from depression is a huge privilege.

I have been a psychiatrist since 1989 and became a Consultant and Senior Lecturer in Old Age Psychiatry in 1995. Throughout the whole of that time, looking after and supporting people with depression has been an ongoing challenge and a privilege. I am also a Catholic. Therefore, what I say in this book is, to some degree, from that perspective. But the reality of what I say is very much applicable to those of all faiths and none.

Faith in a loving God does not protect us from illnesses such as depression. St Thérèse of Lisieux, among many others, shows us that even the holiest people get depression. Many people who suffer with depression carry with them a strong Christian foundation. Good psychiatric and psychological care must never be missing from any healthcare that churches and other voluntary organisations provide.

The primary aim of this book is to help people who are suffering with depression, as well as Christians of all denominations who seek to provide practical and spiritual care for people with depression. But I also hope that it may show the way for those of other faiths and no faith to help people with depression. I hope very much that this little book may help people feel a little more confident as they set off to accompany and help people who suffer from depression.

Depression is an illness that needs the very best treatment. There is much to do and much that good care can achieve.

1

The challenge

What is depression?

Depression is an illness which many people will get at some time in their lives. It is mainly caused by an imbalance of chemicals and chemical receptors in the brain. While it is probably true that everyone is at least a little bit susceptible to depression, some are much more susceptible to it than others. The large part of people's susceptibility to depression is thought to be genetic. Vulnerability to depression is increased by many factors including isolation, unemployment, childbirth, being alone and having no close confidants. Depression is also more common among mothers with young children and in other situations which lead us to be (or feel) isolated and/or unsupported. Physical illnesses, as well as some medications, also make people vulnerable to depression. For example, it is very common after a stroke and in people with dementia.

Following on from, and in addition to, those vulnerabilities, an actual episode of depression may then be triggered by a variety of life events and stressors. Life events include things like marriage, childbirth, getting a new job, losing a job, a diagnosis of illness, bereavement or any other change or event which is significant for an individual. With those triggers, a vulnerable person may become depressed.

What depression is not

Depression is not the same as sadness. We all find ourselves becoming sad when we lose things or friends. If we lose a parent, a spouse, a child or someone who is close to us, for example, we will all go through some sort of bereavement reaction. That may well include sleep loss, a loss of appetite, tearfulness and other symptoms, but those who suffer in that way will normally be able to carry on functioning, sorting out affairs and working, albeit with a little extra time and support. Such episodes will most often resolve over weeks as people continue their daily lives. The ability to carry on does not mean that the loss or other cause of the sadness is less severe. Rather, it means that that individual has been able to cope with that loss without triggering depressive illness. In short, episodes of sadness are common and occur in us all at some time in our lives. Indeed, episodes of sadness are entirely appropriate at times in life.

But depression is different: it has a set of features and is disabling in a way that sadness is not. Importantly, if we think that depression is the same as the episodes of sadness that we have all experienced, we will fail to help and support those who are depressed.

Who gets depression?

Anyone can get depression and the larger the trigger, the more likely we are to develop it. Our brains are extraordinarily complex biological organs which are so sophisticated that they allow us to think, to feel emotion, to understand what is right and wrong and to make choices about what we do. They are the things which, according to our Christian belief, help us to reach the salvation we are promised. But each and every one of us is susceptible to depression if we experience the right triggers. The only proviso to that is that, with age, as we acquire more physical illnesses and as our brain ages, many people do in fact become more susceptible to depression as a result of that ageing.

The biochemistry of depression

Our brains are extraordinarily sophisticated. As part of that sophistication brains have very clever ways of transmitting signals between brain cells. Those signal channels are regulated and modified by complex feedback mechanisms keeping the channels in balance. In mental illnesses such as depression, schizophrenia and even anxiety, those feedback mechanisms go awry and do not work properly. In depression, the receptors for chemicals such as serotonin, noradrenaline, dopamine, glutamate and gamma-aminobutyric acid (GABA) may become altered by having too little (or sometimes too much) of a particular chemical. As a result of that, the receptors adapt themselves to the new environment (a process that is called up- or down-regulation of receptors). That in turn means that the receptors have changed sensitivity to different chemicals and it is those changes that spark the depressive illness itself. Treatments of depression then need to modify these receptors so that they go back towards normal. With that return to their normal sensitivity, depression recovers. Depression is, therefore, firmly built upon a biological foundation and the best treatment is likely to be a combination of medicines, psychological care and lifestyle changes.

Depression is, therefore, in many ways no different from any other sort of physical illness. High blood pressure is a disorder of receptors and chemicals which is treated with a combination of medicines (taken regularly) and lifestyle changes. Treating pneumonia or asthma also requires the right combination of medicines and lifestyle changes. The same goes for many other illnesses. The reality that depression is as real an illness as high blood pressure or pneumonia is not understood by many people. And yet, while almost no one thinks for a moment that high blood pressure or chest infections are caused by some sort of weakness or inadequacy in those who suffer, people often think that depression is the result of some sort of emotional weakness and that the person who has depression is somehow, at least in part, to blame for the reality of their illness. Such assumptions are unfortunate and very unfair.

Depression is as concrete and as real an illness as a chest infection or a broken leg. And yet, there are no physical signs of that illness. The unfortunate lot of those who suffer mental illness is that, lacking clear physical signs of an illness, their suffering is all the more obscure and silent. Such silent, solitary suffering is often extraordinarily painful.

The unfortunate lot of those who suffer mental illness is that, lacking clear physical signs of an illness, their suffering is all the more obscure and silent. Such silent, solitary suffering is often extraordinarily painful.

5

Clinical features and effects of depression

The illness that doctors and nurses call depression has several key features. First and foremost (although not occurring in everyone who has depression) is low mood. A feeling of despair, misery, hopelessness, fear or worry becomes a pervasive component of how people with depression think and the way in which they understand the world around them. In many ways, depression affects the way in which we see things. It is a little like a filter on a painting or a photograph of the things around us. Each image we have of the world around us may be a little greyer, or perhaps a little darker. Each assumption that we make may be just a little bit more negative, or a little bit more despairing.

It is easy to see that in such circumstances, seeing things that little bit more negatively may lead on to thinking things are worse or more hopeless than they actually are. In many ways, that subtly more negative way of seeing and thinking about things is at the core of a depressive illness. Many become more tearful and struggle increasingly with relationships and daily life.

Some people with depression do not suffer with low mood, but the changes in the way they see and feel things may make them more agitated, more worried and more fearful of others.

Alongside those features, people with depression often experience problems with sleep, motivation, appetite and weight loss and also find concentrating on the things that they are doing increasingly hard. These features are often called "biological features of depression". Doctors and nurses often use "biological features" almost as a checklist when deciding if someone has a depression. Interestingly, when some or all of those biological features are present, depression appears to be more likely to respond to antidepressant medication and treatment.

Another key feature of depression is often that the mood is worse at a particular time of day. More often than not, it is worst in the morning and tends to lift during the day and towards evening. As depression recovers with treatment, that lifting of mood towards greater positivity gradually gets earlier and earlier. Some people find that they feel most "down" in the evening or in the afternoon. Whichever time of day their mood is worst, that regular variation of mood during the day is also a predictive feature of a depression that is likely to respond to treatment.

As depression becomes more severe, people find themselves unable to concentrate or cope at work. Withdrawing from work may, in turn, make them more isolated and cause them to feel lower still. But a premature attempt to re-engage someone in work and other activities may well fail to help. Indeed, encouraging them to try to work when they are too sick to do so may be just as counterproductive as sending someone back to work before they have fully recovered from pneumonia or surgery. In the end, a severe depression will most often make people unable to carry on their normal employment for a period of time.

Someone with severe depression may struggle increasingly to think and even to move. Everything about them becomes slowed down, including their thoughts. Depression is an all-embracing illness that affects everything that someone does and thinks. It changes not only the very way in which they think, but also their manner of understanding the world around them and their place in it.

As depression increases in its severity, there is a growing tendency to have thoughts of self-harm and suicide. There is also an increasing frequency of beliefs which are false, with delusions and hallucinations becoming more common.

> Depression is an all-embracing illness that affects everything that someone does and thinks. It changes not only the very way in which they think, but also their manner of understanding the world around them and their place in it.

Key clinical features of depression

Psychological symptoms often include:

- low mood or sadness
- feelings of helplessness and being unable to cope
- poor concentration
- low self-esteem and tearfulness
- irritability, restlessness and being unable to cope with others
- lack of motivation and loss of interest in things
- indecisiveness and feelings of guilt
- inability to enjoy things
- worry and anxiety
- feelings of despair and hopelessness
- thoughts of suicide or self-harm

Physical symptoms often include:

- weight loss, poor appetite or increased appetite
- poor sleep, often with early morning wakening
- constipation
- unexplained aches and pains
- loss of energy
- loss of interest in sex
- changes to women's menstrual cycles
- becoming slowed down in thought processes and movement

Social symptoms often include:

- being unable to work or struggling at work
- being less active, taking less exercise and taking less interest in usual activities and interests
- becoming more isolated
- struggling at home with family and others

Suicide and self-harm

Suicide and self-harm occur quite often in people with depression. Around six thousand people kill themselves each year in Britain and Ireland, and of these about ninety per cent have a serious mental illness. Depression is the most common major mental disorder in people who commit suicide. Alongside suicide, there is a much larger group of people who harm themselves, either with or without the specific intention of killing themselves. Again, the large majority (about ninety per cent) of these people have a mental disorder.

I have already said that depression colours the way in which people think. Depression causes thinking to become more negative: the world seems a little darker and greyer. In attempting to cope with this, people tend to spiral downwards, reaching negative conclusions which can lead to them losing hope and, ultimately, despairing. Some, for example, then lose their jobs as a result of their depression. Others lose relationships or support networks, important factors which contribute to their growing sense of despair and helplessness. There can be a sense of entrapment within decreasing circles of frustration and misery. Life can seem to become a sequence of self-fulfilling prophecies of doom.

In such circumstances, feeling that all around is hopeless, committing suicide can, at times, seem the only logical and practical way out of an impossible situation. In thinking it through, some feel that there is no hope. And so they start to reflect on how they might "end it all" and then perhaps consider why that might be a good thing to do. People with depression do not often kill themselves as soon as they have started having suicidal thoughts. But suicidal thoughts are a very serious sign and a strong indicator of risk. Anyone who expresses suicidal thoughts needs to be offered help and expert care. The act of suicide can require great determination. It will also involve a set of rationalisations which lead people to think that, for example, it is best for their family; that God will understand; that it is better for others and so on.

Depressed thinking can make suicide seem very sensible and appropriate. Depressed people need the care and support of others at times of crisis. If in doubt, always try to enable that help and expert care.

Risk factors for suicide

There are many risk factors for completed suicide. These include:

- a diagnosed mental health condition such as depression

- specific symptoms of depression such as disturbed sleep and feelings of guilt

- alcohol dependence and drug misuse

- a history of trauma or abuse

- unemployment

- being alone and lonely

- poor social conditions and poverty

- imprisonment

- violence and family breakdown

- physical illness, and especially illnesses that lead to immobility, social isolation or physical pain

There are many risk factors for depression: as well as joblessness, homelessness and hopelessness, being older, frail, in pain and isolated also substantially increases the risk. The key point is that anyone who tells you that they are having suicidal thoughts needs to be taken seriously. Make sure that they get some sort of expert help.

Case Study

A thirty-two-year-old single lady who was also a devout Catholic had endured several years of depression without treatment. Her mother also had depression and each month she took two tablets from her mother's bottle of antidepressants. She did not want her mother to notice what she was doing. After two years she had enough tablets to kill herself. She took all of them in one go, along with some sedative tablets. She lay down in bed to die. Very unusually, a relative came home during the day and found her unconscious in bed. He never normally came home at that time and had he not done so she would almost certainly have died.

After resuscitation in hospital she turned out to have a severe depressive illness and clearly remained very determined to kill herself. She said that, having thought about it, God would understand why she did it. Even though she believed suicide to be a mortal sin,* she thought God would understand and still take her to heaven. With treatment, and with time, the depression resolved and she became well again. Her deeply embedded feelings of hopelessness and despair improved. She remained on treatment to prevent further relapses.

Learning points

- Faith in God does not mean that people will not commit suicide, even though they may tell you that they will not kill themselves because they are Christians.

- People who have decided to kill themselves can be very determined.

- With the right initial and ongoing treatment, people can do very well.

- As in this case, it is not uncommon for people to be saved as a result of a very unlikely event. While we must absolutely not rely upon our guardian angels to rescue us, they do (at times) sometimes appear to help us out quite a lot.

* Dying in a state of mortal sin is seen as a way in which someone may lose their chance of salvation and be unable to get to heaven. In this person's case, it seemed that the illness had taken such a hold that the attempt to kill herself was not likely to be such a grave sin. This woman's depressive beliefs were so severe that they had removed her capacity to think clearly and rationally.

Preventing suicide

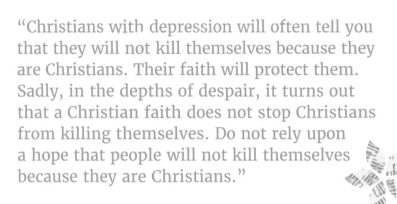

Key factors in suicide prevention are:

- good support and easy access to that support
- ongoing care and being visited and supported by someone
- removing the means of self-harm and suicide
- effective treatment of depression and other major mental illness
- effective medical treatment and pain relief for those with
- significant physical disease
- asking for professional help

"Christians with depression will often tell you that they will not kill themselves because they are Christians. Their faith will protect them. Sadly, in the depths of despair, it turns out that a Christian faith does not stop Christians from killing themselves. Do not rely upon a hope that people will not kill themselves because they are Christians."

Removing access to the means of suicide has considerably helped in the fight to reduce suicides. Examples of success in suicide prevention include the ending of "town gas" (carbon monoxide) supplies into people's homes, catalytic converters (reducing carbon monoxide from car exhausts), reducing the availability of paracetamol in doses large enough to kill and removing ligature points in wards for the acutely mentally unwell. As well as that, just being with someone and providing close specialist monitoring and support during an acute illness does prevent significant numbers of suicides. It's worth remembering therefore, that there are things that we can do to reduce the risk of suicide in those who are unwell. Sometimes, in the most severely at risk, that may require a hospital admission.

False beliefs, hallucinations and psychosis in depression

As I have said, depression colours the way in which we think. It is probably inevitable therefore, that in the more severe depressive illnesses the way people think becomes so distorted that people start to believe things that are not true. A delusion is a belief that is false and also fixed. The belief is not amenable to reason. Common delusions in depression are beliefs of guilt, poverty or being persecuted. As an example, someone who is depressed may become convinced that they have no money and cannot afford to buy food. As a result they eat less and, probably as a result of that, become less well, weaker and more depressed. But simple reasoning and persuasion does not help. And for the person trying to support them that can be very frustrating. In the end, it is the illness that makes these things appear to be true. With treatment of the illness they will settle. Without treatment, any amount of persuasion is unlikely to help.

Case Study

Joseph was a seventy-six-year-old man who had developed a severe depressive illness. Many years ago he had made a mistake on a tax return and as a result he was worried that he owed the taxman money for tax he should have paid in the 1950s. His son went in detail through all his records with him and everything was in order. But he remained convinced that he owed money and that the taxman would be coming after him.

He wrote to the Inland Revenue and offered to pay, but they said they were not worried and that he need not worry either. However, he was still convinced that he had done something wrong. He concluded that his son must have missed something in the paperwork he had looked at. And it was very frustrating for his son to find that, having gone through all the paperwork with him, his father still could not be reassured.

Learning points

- Delusions are fixed false beliefs which are not amenable to reason.

- Delusions can be very disabling.

- It can be very frustrating to find that all efforts to persuade the patient that things are OK fail to make a difference.

Hallucinations also occur in people with severe depression. They may "hear" unpleasant, upsetting and critical voices talking about them.

People always bring themselves, their beliefs and their background to any depressive illness. While our backgrounds are absolutely not the cause of most depressive illnesses, our personalities and beliefs do indeed shape the way in which they present themselves. It is true, therefore, that in all mental illnesses we will tend to form that mental illness around the things that are most important to us in life. People with depression will only rarely become preoccupied about the colour of the wallpaper, for example. Rather, they most often worry that they have no money; that they have done something very wrong; that they are being persecuted; or that they have some dreadful, untreatable illness that is killing them. The point is that all these beliefs and experiences are unpleasant and that the illness most often builds those beliefs and experiences around the things that are most important to the person: the very things that will most often cause the most pain and upset to that individual.

Severe psychotic depression in religious people

People of deep faith will inevitably bring their faith to their illness. I have seen two key types of psychotic depression in people of deep faith.

Delusions of damnation

Some people of faith with severe depression may find their thoughts focusing on things that were done less well in the past, and things that were done which were plainly wrong. But those things then become perceived out of proportion. The confessional stops working as the sin cannot be forgiven. As a result, the person becomes convinced that they are bound to go to hell and cannot be forgiven. There is no hope of redemption.

Case study

Sister Theresa was an eighty-six-year-old retired teacher who had become unwell and severely depressed. She had had depression in the past and had always got better with treatment. This time she was very severely unwell and became convinced that she could not be forgiven. She prayed very hard, almost non-stop, that others might be saved, but believed that she was unforgiveable, and could no longer be saved. The sacrament of reconciliation could not comfort her.

She lost weight and became very frail and weak. She was eating and drinking so little that she was becoming dehydrated. However, she responded to antidepressant medication, Electroconvulsive Therapy (see page 30) and good nursing and made a good recovery.

Learning point

- For some, depression means that the thing they have cherished most (their eventual salvation and life in heaven) seems to have been taken away from them. This is not a failure of faith: rather, it is a result of the deep faith and love that they have for God.

Loss of faith

Others simply lose their faith. All that they have worked for and hoped for becomes worthless and nothing has been achieved. This too can be very distressing. A Salvation Army officer who has worked all her life for the poor and homeless may come to believe in later life that all she did was worthless and pointless, and that the God for whom she so lovingly worked does not exist after all.

Case study

Sister Rita was a seventy-five-year-old retired head teacher who had become unwell and severely depressed. She had a history of bipolar disorder and at times in life had been somewhat elated. But she had built an entire school and been a very able head teacher.

With her depression she became very hopeless, and could not see that anything that she had done had been worthwhile. The school had been all wrong, the pupils not properly taught; she no longer felt that God existed and could not pray. Her life had been pointless and had achieved nothing.

Again, with treatment she improved, regained her faith and went back home to the convent.

Learning point

· For others, depression strips away their faith and their ability to know and feel close to God. Depression is a lonely illness. Again, this loss of faith is not a sign of a weak faith or a bad person. It is the illness changing the way we think and the way we can pray.

It is easy to see that both these forms of depression are dreadfully unpleasant and distressing. And both emphasise the point that the illness of depression is built around the things that the person with depression holds most dear.

Bipolar disorder

Formerly known as manic depression, bipolar disorder is a form of depression which is both recurrent and also associated with mood swings and episodes of overconfidence and elation. As well as having recurrent episodes of depression, being "high" or elated can lead to considerable problems. Some patients spend too much money running up debts, which need to be paid off when they are better. Others just give money away or engage in risky behaviours. And despite what you might think, being "high" is not very nice. It comes with feelings of pressure and fatigue, as well as (for some) feelings of being out of control.

Depression after childbirth

Severe depressions also occur after childbirth. Postpartum psychosis is an especially severe form of depression which appears to be triggered by the emotional effect of giving birth alongside the large and significant hormonal changes that occur at that time. It is a very severe form of depression which requires urgent and excellent care.

What happens to people who are depressed?

The prognosis (or longer-term outcome) of depression can be very good with the right treatment. People who are depressed and who accept treatment can do well, get better and return to work. The important thing is to find the right help and the right treatment when it is needed.

Clearly it is absolutely essential to protect people and to keep them from killing themselves. Preventing suicide and providing really good support is the key to recovery. People who are seriously suicidal may need someone to be with them twenty-four hours a day and may need hospital treatment to ensure their safety. But generally, within weeks or months, most people will make a good recovery and get back to their usual lives and patterns of work.

After recovery, relapse of depression is common. Relapse may happen as a result of crises or new life events. That said, people who have had a depressive illness are probably always at higher risk of a relapse. So for those who have had a severe depressive illness, it is a very good idea to think about some ongoing treatment to prevent relapse.

> After recovery, relapse of depression is common... so for those who have had a severe depressive illness, it is a very good idea to think about some ongoing treatment to prevent relapse.

Case study

June suffered an acute and severe depression in her forties. After recovery she was placed on a medicine called lithium to prevent relapse. She stayed on this medication for thirty years. Now that she was in her seventies, her GP (sensibly) thought that perhaps she ought to stop the lithium as it can have some effects on the kidneys. Within three months of stopping the lithium June had a serious relapse needing several weeks in hospital, and from which she only recovered slowly over months thereafter.

Learning point

- Ongoing treatment can be very helpful in terms of preventing a relapse of depression.

Does depression cause long-term harm and side effects?

Sadly, some will (as a result of the illness) have lost their job, or the support of close friends or family. In those circumstances it is easy to see that the effects of an acute episode of illness can create long-lasting challenges in people's lives.

Depression causes loss of motivation and interest in life. Especially in older people, that leads on to inactivity, weight loss, doing less, going out less and isolation. As well as that, some of the medications used to treat severe depression may have side effects which reduce mobility and increase the risk of falls. Put together, this means that, especially in older people, depression can be really very harmful, making people substantially more frail and leaving them with long-term and permanent harms. This is all the more reason why we need to work hard to treat people with depression as quickly and effectively as we can – and also to think about ongoing medication to prevent relapse. It is too easy to stop an antidepressant while forgetting to think through why stopping treatment may be harmful.

> Especially in older people, depression can be really very harmful, making people substantially more frail and leaving them with long-term and permanent harms. This is all the more reason why we need to work hard to treat people with depression as quickly and effectively as we can.

The need to save life and to impose treatment

At times depression becomes so severe that people believe they cannot be helped and that there is no hope. Some begin to hallucinate and hear voices (usually unpleasant or critical). Others may believe that they are dying of cancer when they are well. Still more become convinced that they must kill themselves as there is no other option. Sadly, such people will often also conclude that doing so will be better for their family or help others. In all these circumstances, people become so unwell that they are no longer able to make a real choice about what to do. Their understanding has become so distorted by their illness that they can no longer see reality – and their decisions become driven by the false reality which their illness shows them.

The Mental Health Act

In these circumstances, urgent specialist help is required. Usually, patients will agree to an admission to hospital for treatment and care (including their protection from self-harm). If necessary, however, some will require compulsory admission under the Mental Health Act. That act and those orders for admission (sections) are carefully set up by psychiatrists working alongside another approved mental health professional (AMHP). Together they have the power and duty to detain for admission and treatment people who are too unwell to accept the care and treatment they require. Alongside that, there is an appeals mechanism which is available to anyone detained under the Mental Health Act and that works as an effective safeguard against a wrong or unnecessary decision to impose treatment.

The Mental Capacity Act and Common Law

When someone needs to be admitted for treatment under the Mental Health Act, it needs to be achieved as soon as possible. But while that is being done and before the Mental Health Act has been applied, anyone can take reasonable measures to protect and support someone with a severe depression. As long as what is done is to protect their lives, to protect others or to protect the long-term health of that individual, reasonable restraint, support and at times the administration of medicine can be delivered. In brief, the Mental Capacity Act is used to protect and treat those who are reasonably thought to be so ill that they cannot make a valid choice. Common Law may be required to restrain a person to prevent harm to others.

The key point here is that we all have a duty of care to those who are very unwell. And we have a duty to act when people are so unwell that they are at risk or unable to make a valid choice about their healthcare. While acting in the short term to protect life and health, we must also do all we can to make sure that specialist help is sought.

Different cultures and depression

As with all mental illnesses, depression forms itself around the individual who has the illness. The most important things for the individual tend to occupy their thoughts. That is why, for example, Christians with depression find that depression involves and affects their faith, their families and their Christian service.

Our cultural background also affects how depression presents. An example of this is depression in people from Asia. It is widely held that some people from Asia present with more physical symptoms such as headaches, sweating, tremors and pain. That is a vast generalisation but also, to a degree, probably true. Some people just do not present with low mood and do not recognise negative thoughts and feelings, but they do suffer greatly and complain of pain. It is absolutely true that some cultures struggle to understand and integrate depression as a concept into their language and ways of life.

Some people with depression may also complain more of physical symptoms than low mood. In some workplaces and other settings it is easier to complain of pain than it is to admit that you are being treated for depression.

It is equally or even more true that in the business world depression can be lethal to a career. I was once told that airline pilots who are depressed lose their licence. While it is absolutely right to protect airline passengers from being flown by depressed and suicidal pilots, the negative effect of such a rule would be that pilots dare not admit to depression for fear of unemployment.

Culture and the background from which we come can profoundly affect the way a depressive illness presents.

2

Treatments for depression

Depression is a treatable condition from which we hope for a good recovery. It does cause long-term harm, especially because of the ways in which it disrupts our relationships, our work and our livelihoods. Many of those long-term harms are made worse by more severe and more slowly treated depressive illnesses. As a rule of thumb, mild and moderate depressive illnesses may well respond to psychological treatments. Severe depressions will also need medication and other treatments.

Effective psychological and supportive treatments of depression

Behavioural therapies and cognitive behavioural therapies have established themselves as effective ways of treating depression. By analysing the problem and seeing what is causing a negative way of thinking, real change and understanding can bring effective help to people with mild and moderate depressive illnesses.

Behavioural psychotherapy is a little less widely used than cognitive behavioural therapy. But behavioural therapy essentially uses doing things and activities to treat a difficulty. For example, some people who develop a great fear of going out or interacting with others may be helped simply by a programme that encourages them to do just that, but within their abilities. With success, their abilities grow and their depression recedes. Behavioural therapies are also very helpful in obsessive compulsive disorders.

It is easy to condemn. Doing so can be very harmful. Tolerance, compassion, understanding, support and empathy are absolutely essential.

Counselling and support

Counselling and just providing the space to talk and think is also helpful for milder depression. Most healthcare trusts now provide counselling services for people with depression. These are well used and patients value them. For many with mild depression or depression with prominent anxiety, counselling may be very helpful. There are also some Christian counsellors and counselling organisations.

But there are also some concerns with counselling. Sadly, at times, counsellors do not appear to understand people's faith background. As a result I hear of patients who feel unsupported and criticised in their faith by counselling. Counselling is said to be non-judgemental but, in fact, that is not really true at all. No counsellor would refuse to take action if he or she were told that the patient was about to go and do something dreadful such as killing someone else. But in some circumstances (perhaps severe distress following an abortion) patients find that a non-judgemental approach may appear to dismiss their belief that what they did (for example, the abortion) was wrong. Patients who wish to take their value system to counselling may not find that that is quite fully understood by the counsellor.

Alongside all of those psychological therapies sits ongoing care, support and gentle advice. Such help can be truly life-changing and is very much part of what Christian churches and Christians in the workplace should feel able to offer to their friends and colleagues. The sacrament of reconciliation also provides a set of places where things can be discussed and real, practical help given in company with the forgiveness of sins.

Case study

Jim has become depressed. As a result he has lost motivation, has not been sleeping and has spent too long on his iPad. His house is untidy, he has not eaten properly and the garden is now overgrown. The grass gets longer every day.

A behavioural therapy plan might encourage him to cut the grass and tidy the house, or perhaps to help him do this so that he becomes confident again in doing it.

A cognitive behavioural strategy might start by helping him to understand why he feels he cannot do these things, to encourage him to do them and to thus rebuild ability and confidence.

Learning points

- Behavioural and cognitive behavioural therapies may be very effective in treating depression, building confidence as they go.

- Such therapies fit neatly alongside a concept of free will and the ability that we all have to develop from where we are, and to move forward with the difficulties we have.

Treatments for which there is little evidence of benefit or which may harm

Some psychotherapies in particular do not really have much evidence of benefit for the individual. Freudian psychoanalytic psychotherapy is based upon a belief that we are determined by our past and that we cannot change unless we go right back to our early and formative years. As a result, therapy is prolonged, often slow and may have negative consequences as well. Even Freud found that therapy did not go well. One of his patients (whom he called the Wolf Man) remained in therapy for nearly seventy years.

Other therapies may also be less than effective. Rogerian therapy sees everything the patient does in a positive light. But, of course, if you do that, you cannot see things in a negative light. Therefore, it cannot really provide a set of solutions to some of the very real problems that people bring to therapy. Such therapies do not always sit well alongside the Christian concepts of good, evil, sin and virtue. If everything is good, then nothing is bad.

Some other therapeutic regimes may also be less than helpful. If the therapies focus upon the wrong things, or if they encourage the wrong behaviours, beliefs or thought structures, they may be harmful. As with any treatment, therapies will have positive and negative effects.

The philosophical basis of psychotherapies

It is worth being aware of the underlying philosophical basis of the various psychotherapies available.

Some therapies (including behavioural therapies and cognitive behavioural therapies) seem to fit alongside Christian concepts of free will, development and growth. And they seem to work well.

Some other therapies (including psychoanalysis) have a fundamentally determinist basis to them. That is, they assume (as did Freud) that we are products of our biology and our past. That does not always seem to fit easily alongside Christian concepts of free will, development and growth. It is worrying that some people receiving these therapies have been known to lose their faith during therapy. A number of religious orders who embraced determinist forms of psychotherapy in the 1970s are said to have seen many nuns or priests lose their faith and leave.

> Some therapies have a fundamentally determinist basis to them... that does not always seem to fit easily alongside Christian concepts of free will, development and growth... Some people receiving these therapies have been known to lose their faith during therapy.

Medical treatment of depression

Drug treatment

The mainstay of treatment for depression is antidepressant medicines. These medicines have undergone a quiet revolution over the last thirty years. Before the availability of drugs, depression was a devastating illness which took away people's livelihoods and which (in those who did not die from the illness) could also lead to a lifetime of institutionalisation. Without treatment, some suffered severe and extreme psychosis. Others simply would not eat, wasted away and died. Others recovered but were weakened both biologically and socially.

The advent of the first antidepressants was transformational. Within as little as a fortnight, improvement would be seen and people started to recover. While it always took a lot longer to recover fully, it is compelling to watch severely depressed people starting to eat and drink again, beginning to smile once more and starting to do things again.

The first generation of antidepressants were highly effective medicines which were thought of as needing a couple of weeks to start working. Tricyclic antidepressant medicines such as amitriptyline, clomipramine and trimipramine became widely used. But they did have some quite serious side effects. They commonly caused symptoms such as a dry mouth, confusion, low blood pressure and blurred vision. The treatment itself produced side effects that were disabling. Less commonly it could cause falls, hallucinations and heart rhythm disturbances. Most seriously of all (unlike modern antidepressants), the first generation antidepressants were very dangerous in overdose, as they caused the heart to stop and be very difficult to restart. As a result, some depressed people would kill themselves using the very medicines that they had been given to make them better. Indeed, it is thought that the risk of suicide may increase when people are starting to recover: they get a sense of energy back which is sometimes associated with attempts at suicide.

> The risk of suicide may increase when people are starting to recover: they get a sense of energy back which is sometimes associated with attempts at suicide.

29

Other early antidepressants were equally problematic. But they were also effective and could transform lives. As has always been the case, each individual person with depression is different and getting the medicines right has always needed some trial and error.

Newer antidepressants were first introduced in the 1980s. They have fewer side effects and are much safer in overdose. Most widely used among them are the selective serotonin reuptake inhibitors (SSRIs) or Prozac-like medicines. These antidepressants specifically block receptors for a chemical called serotonin. They may work a little more slowly, but with fewer side effects they can be taken for a longer period while a person's recovery consolidates.

As well as those drugs, there are now many more options. A large variety of different antidepressants are supported by other medicines to help improve mood. The really good news is that nowadays, with the right help, enough time and the right medications, failure to recover from depression is uncommon.

Lithium and anticonvulsant medicines are worth a special mention. Lithium is highly effective and stabilises the membranes of brain cells. It can produce excellent improvements and is also very useful in terms of preventing relapse of depression and in preventing mania in people with bipolar disorder. Lithium needs special and careful monitoring. Too much is dangerous and too little does not work. Anticonvulsant medicines when used for depression work in a way similar to lithium.

Electroconvulsive Therapy (ECT)

Electroconvulsive Therapy (ECT) is a very effective, but also controversial treatment. It involves a brief anaesthetic; while the patient is asleep a brain seizure (or fit) is induced using an electrical impulse.

Many are deeply concerned about the use of ECT and there is a widespread availability of material on the internet that shares those concerns. But actually it works well and can be truly life-saving for the right person.

Most commonly, ECT is used when people are very unwell, perhaps when they are psychotic with false beliefs or when they are barely eating or drinking. ECT can cause side effects of confusion and headache but studies have shown that these do resolve with time. Some patients who have had it never want it again. Many more, in studies, say they would want it again if necessary.

Case study

Andrew, an eighty-year-old man, had a lifelong history of relapsing, really quite severe depressions. A delightful and gentle man, when unwell he was profoundly psychotic, feeling that his wife was at risk and at times feeling that his eyes should be removed to prevent him from coming to harm. He also felt that he ought to kill his wife to protect her.

He responded very slowly and incompletely to antidepressants. With a course of ECT he improved but complained of confusion. After discharge from hospitals he continued to be moderately poorly (though far better than he had been when acutely unwell). Finally he was started on lithium and made a rapid and good improvement.

He went home and continued his active life as a husband, father and grandfather and a member of his local church. He remained well for several years. For him, it was wise to just carry on the medicines life-long.

Learning points

- Some people with depression will stay well for many years after treatment.

- Relapses can occur and can be severe.

- Getting better involves time and the right treatment.

- Life-long treatment to prevent relapse is right for some people.

Case study

Mary had a severe depression and was barely eating and drinking. She was eighty-five and very frail, and believed that there was no hope either for her survival or for her salvation. She believed she had sinned so badly that she could not be forgiven.

Antidepressants had not worked (as she was not swallowing them) and there was real concern that her fluid intake was so low she was at risk of serious physical deterioration. ECT led to a marked and rapid improvement. She ate breakfast and drank after the first treatment and made further progress, being able to go home after a few weeks.

Learning points

- ECT is a controversial treatment about which many have concerns.

- It is also very effective and can truly save life in some people.

Spiritual support

Although some people with the most severe depressions lose their faith while they are depressed, most do not. Spiritual support, as well as the fellowship and friendship of friends, priests and pastors, is an essential component of care for people who are depressed. For those who normally pray, accompaniment during prayer may be very helpful. Depressed people will struggle to pray in a way that others do not. Someone who, for example, prays the rosary or other familiar prayers regularly when they are well may need the help and company of a friend when they are unwell.

Spiritual care must *only* ever be offered gently and carefully. At a time of vulnerability and illness, it is given to us to care and support. But we must not impose faith or duty. Neither should we accept the loss of access to spiritual support at a moment of such great need. Care, humility, kindness, charity and tact are absolutely essential.

Spiritual support is a vital component of the help we can offer to people with depression. But remember, spiritual care and support should work alongside other appropriate medical care and therapy. It does not replace it.

The sacraments and depression

Holy Communion

The Church teaches that the sacraments bring graces for those who receive them, regardless of any illness from which a person may be suffering. Therefore, it can be a good and helpful thing for people with depression to continue to receive the Eucharist. Sometimes severe delusions of guilt may make them feel unworthy and, for very deluded people, if you encourage them too strongly, you may cause a worsening in their guilt after they have received Holy Communion. But generally it is helpful to be able to continue to receive it. As well as benefiting from the graces that come via the sacrament, people with depression may well feel comforted by being able to maintain the practice of their faith.

Reconciliation

The sacrament of reconciliation can be a very powerful help in depression. Most priests will have seen people who are really suffering and for whom the gift of forgiveness brings great hope and relief.

Reconciliation can be part of the healing process during recovery. Of course, in a serious depressive illness, alone, it will not cure the illness.

There are a few things to note:

- Confession will not cure depression: depression is an illness and confession can assist in recovery but it is unlikely to be the cure.

- Sometimes depression heightens people's awareness of sinfulness or of serious errors that have happened in earlier life.

- Some very depressed people ask repeatedly for forgiveness of a particular sin. A valid confession forgives sin once and for all. Repeated confessions are not required unless the sin is committed again. If people with depression repeatedly confess the same sin, it may be worthwhile just reassuring them that they have already confessed and received absolution for that sin.

- Some very depressed people seek forgiveness for things which are not sins or sins which they never committed at all.

- Occasionally, depressed people may seek the sacrament of reconciliation as often as daily. This may not be entirely helpful. Careful pastoral discernment by the confessor may be needed.

But the sacrament of reconciliation can be a real help. And for some, it can be truly transformative. There are also many other forms of spiritual care and support which we can and should offer to those who want that care.

"The sacrament of
reconciliation can be
a real help. And for
some, it can be truly
transformative. There
are also many other
forms of spiritual care
and support which we can
and should offer to those
who want that care."

3

For those who suffer

The experience of being depressed

The experience of depression is always unique to the individual who suffers. We bring ourselves to the illness: the ways we think, the things we value and so much more. As well as that, the illness itself varies between individuals. The loss of hope will often focus upon the things that that individual values the most. Some become withdrawn and turn in upon themselves. Others become agitated and worried and others angry. The stories of different patients throughout this book give some idea of the variety of ways in which depression does what it does. But it would be impossible to make a reasonable list of all the different ways in which people suffer with depression. Those stories are as varied and numerous as the individuals who suffer.

That simple fact does tell us one thing. When we are seeking to support people with depression we often feel drawn towards sharing some of our experience as a means of encouragement. But we must always remember that because depression is so varied, those reassurances may just fail to "gel" with the person who suffers. And at times, such attempts may just make them feel more forlorn and alone.

"When I was depressed I just dreaded each day. I wanted to die and did things more recklessly than I ever normally would. Things like crossing the road. Eating was a problem. I knew that food keeps you well. And I did not really want to stay well."

"I could not study, and would watch films late into the night. I got behind at college and as a result got more depressed. Studying I found impossible. I lost weight, and could not face meeting or seeing anyone."

Depression is an unpleasant experience in which things just seem worse. Hope, energy and motivation gradually drift away and then disappear. Despite that, people with depression think logically and sensibly, but think things through in the light of what they see and know. All that they see and know is, in turn, coloured by the reality of their depression. As a result, negative conclusions are reached which can look very inaccurate to those who look on. But support and persuasion do not resolve the issues and difficulties.

"It was a Saturday lunchtime. I suddenly realised that I could understand why people could commit suicide. I couldn't get away from 'me' and 'me' hurt so much. I longed to escape from 'me' and I couldn't."

"I was born to be a skylark, soaring above the earth and bursting its little heart in song. Instead, I was a chicken, trapped in a cage, pecking at the ground. I could see the sky but I couldn't escape. Even if someone had released me, it would have been useless: I'd forgotten how to fly."

"I couldn't see that anything I did had a value. It seemed as though people were nice to me because they were nice. I couldn't see that I might be lovable and that they might be responding to goodness within me."

Others become very aware that they are not able to cope at work or in challenging situations. They therefore withdraw to a comfort zone where they are not stretched in any way. In that place, people look for comfort and may find this in isolation, on the internet and in many other ways, all of which may not, in the end, help at all.

Hopelessness

Hopelessness is a difficult and grave experience. Many of us, at times, lack hope and fear bad things. But while we might lack hope, we rarely see no hope at all. Many people believe that when we suffer we can find opportunities to pray for others and to come closer to Jesus. That is perfectly true. Among those who have no faith, many will also hope that that some good can emerge through the hardship and suffering.

But at the most difficult times things become much harder. In very difficult situations and in very severe depressions, people lose the ability to see that things may get better, or that there is any hope. In Christian thinking, this is sometimes seen as a call for abandonment to divine providence. When, in the nineteenth century, Fr Jean Pierre de Caussade SJ wrote his work of spiritual direction, *Abandonment to Divine Providence*, he saw that such abandonment would be a joyful trust in our Saviour. But in depression, in the depths of hopelessness, there will be no such joy. Rather the very notion that we can trust in a loving Saviour is eroded and removed. Despair is an unpleasant thing indeed. But it is also common in depression.

We must, therefore, support people who are depressed and nurture them through the depths of their despair in this very difficult illness.

Inability to work and inability to cope

A lot can be done to help people carry on working. If that can be done, it is probably a good thing. Keeping in work keeps all sorts of good things going. But in moderate and more severe depressions, work becomes exhausting, overwhelming and impossible.

Functioning at home also becomes hard and that can be very difficult for people who have responsibilities such as children and others for whom they have to care. Work becomes harder because depression compromises energy, motivation and concentration.

The need for support

For all the reasons above, it is very important that we gently and humbly support people who have depression. Ongoing care, accompaniment and also just basic support such as making sure there is food available are essential components of the care we give.

As I have already said on page 33, spiritual support is a vital component of the help we can offer to people with depression. But remember, spiritual care and support should work alongside other appropriate medical care and therapy. It does not replace it. Nor can it be imposed. Care, humility, kindness, charity and tact are absolutely essential.

The need for respect

Support must be given with a real sense of respect and care. When people are unwell and vulnerable it is easy to decide to impose a solution. But that imposition may well turn out to be unhelpful, especially if it feels like an imposition to someone who is unwell. At times though, imposition of care is essential (see page 21). For example, if someone is suicidal it is our duty to protect them and not allow them to kill themselves during the depths of their illness and while they recover.

"It is very important that
we gently and humbly
support people who have
depression. Ongoing care,
accompaniment and also just
basic support such as making
sure there is food available
are essential components of
the care we give."

4

For those who care

Caring for someone with depression can be really hard work and, at times, a terrifying experience. That is perhaps especially so when someone is suicidal as a result of their depression. Inevitably, anyone who supports someone with depression will (at least every now and then) get it wrong, say the wrong thing or be too distant or supportive in the wrong way. While we must be careful not to get it wrong, we must also be careful to carry on caring and supporting.

Case study

Geraldine, a twenty-seven-year-old woman who worked as a university researcher became depressed, struggling with work and a very low self-esteem. Her quality of sleep had deteriorated. She could not concentrate or cope with her work and felt very down. She felt a lot worse in the mornings. Extensive support from her family and others helped, but she was not getting better. Continuing that support along with an antidepressant medicine led to real improvement. She returned to her work and stopped her antidepressants after about a year. She subsequently remained well.

Learning points

- Be aware of risk.

- Good support and care can make a real difference.

- As depression becomes more severe, the right medication can enable the patient to respond to the care and support offered.

- Stopping medicines too soon can be harmful and lead to relapse but, with medical advice, most people who have had a single episode of depression can leave them off after about six to twelve months.

Supporting people with depression

Often enough, just being with someone, being sympathetic and being supportive, is the right thing to do. Making sure there is food; supporting someone in carrying on daily activities; practical help with children when someone is very poorly, or perhaps when they need to go to a hospital appointment, may also be very helpful. But in the end there are no rules. Each person with depression is an individual who needs their own, unique support structure.

Talking things through

It is right to sit and talk things though with people who are depressed. It is also right to reassure people about things that are troubling them greatly (as long as that reassurance is not dishonest, of course). But there are real problems that arise from that desire to reassure and encourage. Comments like "when I was depressed I found that... helped me a lot" or "when I was depressed I did..." may feel helpful at the time but can in fact be very hurtful. Specific advice and an attempt to share experiences may backfire. Each depressed person's illness is unique. Therefore, any past experiences you have may be less helpful than they seem.

Sharing the "I did this and got better" ideas often fails because our experience does not translate into the experience of others. What has worked for you may fail for others and, in failing, that advice may make things worse. Advice and encouragement, perhaps, to take exercise or do something else may be good advice, but you may well find it is best to just gently encourage rather than saying how you "managed to do it even though it was hard". That simply invites a deeper sense of failure. Then the depressed person concludes that they are not as strong as you were when you were struggling with depression.

People have often said something like, "God loves you so much, so you ought to be happy." This is fine and is also true in a way. But depressed people are unwell and cannot be happy. If we tell them that God wants them to be happy and therefore they *should* be happy, it merely makes things worse. It may well make them feel further from God and even deeper failures. Faced with such "encouragement", some have simply concluded that they were never Christians and have no hope.

Giving hope

As I have said, depression is an illness that so often erodes and
eliminates hope. It may well be impossible to offer hope to those who
are in the depths of despair. But, more usually, ongoing care, concern,
support, and just gentle compassion can be truly life-saving and hold
a person while they start their journey towards recovery. Indeed, we
are very much creatures of hope. That sense of both emotional and
practical care and support can, at times, go a long way to instilling
hope and giving people the strength to bear the burden of their
depression. We will most often do this by practical support, discussion
and accompaniment.

Prayer

As well as giving practical and emotional support we will also pray
for those who are depressed. Of course, as people who believe
in God, we can and should pray for anyone whom we feel needs
prayers. We need not seek the permission of that person. But the
prayer we make is a private prayer; a prayer between ourselves and
God. The person for whom we pray need not know that they are
being prayed for. What we say to and what we ask of God in our
hearts is entirely private and belongs to ourselves. It's just that we
trust that (when he sees fit) others will benefit as a result of his
response to those prayers. And for those of us who are working as
professionals, we must also ensure that whether or not we pray for
someone, the care given is of the highest standard.

At other times, Christians may well want to pray with people,
using either set prayers or free-form prayers. For some this may
be saying the rosary; for others the Lord's Prayer; reading the
Psalms or just being in church may be right and appropriate.
Going to church services or receiving the sacraments (as set out
above) may also be very helpful. What we do and the way we do
it will vary depending upon whether or not we have a professional
or a friendship-based relationship with the individual.
But either way, we should not impose prayer or faith
upon any individual.

Professionals are in a position of authority and power. Therefore, they must be careful if a patient asks them to pray with them or for them. They must ensure that any prayer or other support they give does not enable or cause any misuse of their power and authority. Great care, gentleness and careful thought are required along with careful adherence to their professional code of practice.

On the other hand we know and believe that prayer and the sacraments bring real graces and real changes to people who are sick. To deny a request for prayer would be very hard. It is surely wrong not to offer depressed people any opportunity to think through issues of faith.

When we do discuss faith and prayer with depressed individuals, we must be sure that that discussion is wanted, and that we discuss supportively, without imposing our faith or prayers upon people who are depressed, just at the time of their greatest vulnerability.

The burden of caring

Caring for people with any illness can be very hard. Long and detailed chats about why things may be not quite so bad, ongoing support and just trying to both protect and keep people safe and going can require a lot of effort. And then, after all that effort, carers themselves may struggle when the person with depression continues to be just as forlorn and lacking in hope. All the effort invested feels as if it has come to nothing.

As with all caring, being mindful of doing enough and being generous, while not becoming exhausted and overreached, is important. The carer must also stay well and protect their resilience. There are many resources and support groups available for carers, associated with almost all the mental health charities and accessible via the NHS. The churches must also support their carers.

In the UK, carers for people with both physical and mental health conditions are entitled (by law) to a carer's assessment of their needs.

4. For those who care

Fear of self-harm

When people are expressing thoughts of self-harm and suicide, this can be very scary for carers who may well end up feeling responsible. It is, of course, really important to protect the individual with depression. And, therefore, this really is a good stage to be ensuring that professional advice has been sought. As I have already said, when the risk of self-harm is high, a hospital admission may be required.

Accompaniment and support

Depression is an illness that calls us (as people who care) to accompany those who are sick. We are called to just be there, supporting, and (at the right times) encouraging. Sometimes it may be right to give kindly advice. The care we give shows whether or not we do indeed care. And having family, friends, clergy and health professionals for support is an invaluable part of people's journey through depression.

Being human, we will often hope that what we do will fix the problem and make things better. At times, this does indeed turn out to be the case. At other times, despite that accompaniment, large amounts of care and support may well seem to be of no use. Sometimes, things may seem to have become even worse.

Case study

Joan has been suffering on and off with depression for many years. At the moment she is really struggling and her daughter Jane is visiting often and supporting her. She has seen her GP and has also seen the mental health team. But despite all the care and help, she is just not getting better. Jane feels it has all been of no avail and worries that she may even be making things worse. Her efforts have certainly not led to recovery just yet. But if she withdraws, her mother does not eat and seems to languish even more.

Perhaps here, Joan needs:

- a review of her care and treatment by the specialists;

- the ongoing support of her daughter and perhaps of some other people.

And Jane just needs the support and encouragement to be able to continue to cope with the frustration of her mother's ongoing illness.

Occasionally it may be necessary to stand back. But just as with other mental illnesses (including dementia and schizophrenia) the need for accompaniment means that we may well need to just keep supporting and trying to help. Sometimes, as a result of the support we give, we can see real benefits.

At other times after a lot of effort trying to care and support, it can be very frustrating and dispiriting to think that little or nothing has been achieved. That is when ongoing accompaniment and support can be so important. If and when people do seem to be stuck, a review of care and treatment may be very helpful.

"Having family, friends, clergy and health professionals for support is an invaluable part of people's journey through depression."

5

Depression and sin

Sin is something that we all do and of which we are called to try and do less. Interestingly, we often commit sins because we hope to gain something out of doing so. For example, robbery may make us richer, or hurting someone else may make us more secure. But in the end, sin has negative effects and consequences. Living with the consequence of our actions and sins can be very hard and lead to despair.

Many of the harmful things that we do are not sins. We do them unknowingly, unintentionally or by accident. To sin requires a decision to do wrong. In depression and especially in severe depressions when people are psychotic, the things that we might think are always sins may not be so.

Think for a moment about the story of Gary overleaf. Murder is a sin. Attempted murder is also clearly a sin. But did Gary sin here? Depression clouds the mind and colours the thinking. His experience had made him incredibly angry with his mother. Now think about the answers to the questions posed.

God knows when we sin and also knows when what we do is driven by mental illness and an inability to understand. God can and does, in the end, judge. He is the just judge. But we cannot judge. We know with certainty that trying to kill our mother is deeply wrong. But for Gary, we do not know if it was a sin.

Case study

Gary had become very depressed, lost his job, drank too much and also turned to drugs for comfort. Arrested by the police, he believed that he was being deliberately persecuted and became very angry. His mother tried really hard to help but in the end he heard voices telling him that she was on the side of the police and the hospital. He tried to kill his mother.

Questions

- Were Gary's actions objectively morally wrong?

- Were his actions driven by his illness?

- Had he lost the power to understand what was being done and why?

- What if some of his care had been less than perfect?

- Is he truly fully responsible for the attempt to murder his mother?

- Did he sin?

Now think for a moment about Zoe. Did she sin? It seems very unlikely that she did.

Case study

Zoe became acutely depressed and psychotic a few days after giving birth to her first daughter, Rachel. She began to believe that "the spirits" would possess her daughter who would become trapped for ever, destined for an eternity in hell. The spirits would then also take her. Zoe set fire to the house, killing herself and her child. The note she left said it was the only option left to her. Otherwise she could not protect her daughter.

Question

- Did Zoe's illness so powerfully colour her thinking that she was only in fact acting out of a false belief that her actions were necessary to protect her daughter?

The sacrament of reconciliation is both a place where sins can be forgiven and a place where things that are not, in fact, sins can be thought through.

6

Some mistakes we make

1. With prayer you may not need medicines

There is often a strong reluctance to take antidepressant and other medicines for mental illness. In that context, people often hope that prayer, being strong, or just kindness and support from others will be enough.

In severe depressions, supporting such a view can be very unhelpful and end up meaning that someone becomes stuck in a longer-lasting and untreated depression. Worse still, avoidable suicide might occur. It can be a very serious mistake to support someone in prayer alone if the result of that is to keep them from effective treatments.

There are many alternate forms of this mistake which is repeatedly made both by people of faith and no faith. Just giving support, using homeopathies, herbal remedies and other dietary changes have all been tried. Without medicines all of these approaches can, at times go very badly.

Suffice to say that prayer can be a vital and strong part of recovering from depression. But do not think of it as the only thing that is needed. If it enables the avoidance of necessary treatment, the results may be disastrous.

2. "If you have no hope then you haven't found Jesus!"

I recently saw this message on a banner outside a church, and felt it was just an example of how badly we can, as Christians, get it wrong. Seeing this could have deeply hurt a depressed Christian, who might well have gone away concluding that, in lacking hope, they had lost the very thing they treasured most. It's important to be careful about what we say and how we say it. With the best intentions, this message is often shared with people who are depressed. Doing so can backfire quite badly.

3. *Becoming frustrated and cross*

With a lot of effort and persuasion we all hope to see an improvement. Sometimes, those efforts fail and depression does not easily respond. At times it may feel as if the person with depression is being wilfully awkward. Remember that it is the illness that frustrates our efforts to help. At such times getting cross is almost always a bad idea and to be avoided if possible.

Case study

Jack developed a late-life depression and became convinced that he would be arrested for tax fraud and that he was bankrupt. After many hours of persuasion that things were not as bad as they seemed, his son had gone through all his accounts and shown with certainty that Jack's finances were fine.

Jack commented: "There's something you have missed. I am sure I am bankrupt."

His poor son realised that all those hours of persuasion had just failed. It is easy to get cross at this stage. Being cross rarely helps.

At times it may feel as if the person with depression is being wilfully awkward. Remember that it is the illness that frustrates our efforts to help. At such times getting cross is almost always a bad idea and to be avoided if possible.

4. Doing too much and then having to withdraw

Overpromising is likely to mean that we underdeliver. Be careful to be sure that you can deliver and sustain what you set out to do. When we find we are struggling and if we have to withdraw, that can be very hard for the person whom we sought to help.

Conclusion

Depression is an unpleasant illness which changes the way we think, the way we hope and the way we live. Depression causes great suffering. It does not have the external signs of illness that are seen with physical illnesses. Depression is a huge call for the care, support and charity of Christian organisations and Christian people.

It is important to know about the illness and to be especially aware of the dangers that come with depression, such as self-neglect, self-harm and suicide. It is also good to be aware of the ways in which we can get the help and care we offer wrong.
For those who suffer, we can and must care.

7

Prayers and reflections

Behold the Cross of the Lord!
(Ecce Crucis Domine)

Fly, you powers of darkness!
The Lion of Judah,
The Root of Jesse,
Has conquered you!
Alleluia!

Prayer of St Ignatius of Loyola

O Christ Jesus,
When all is darkness
And we feel our weakness and helplessness,
Give us the sense of your presence,
Your love and your strength.
Help us to have perfect trust
In your protecting love
And strengthening power,
So that nothing may frighten or worry us,
For, living close to you,
We shall see your hand,
Your purpose, your will through all things.

Resources and references

Books and journals

M. Dominic Beer and Nigel D. Pocock (eds) *Mad, Bad or Sad?: a Christian approach to antisocial behaviour and mental disorder* (Christian Medical Fellowship, 2006)

Useful websites

https://www.acc-uk.org

The Association of Christian Counsellors facilitates provision by Christians of quality counselling and pastoral care and holds an accredited register for Christian counsellors.

http://inspiritedminds.org.uk/

Inspirited Minds works with people suffering from psychological illnesses, predominantly, though not exclusively, from an Islamic faith. It was initiated as a result of findings that there was limited help available for Muslim sufferers and many people found it difficult to seek help as they felt they would not be understood by someone who did not understand their faith or culture.

https://www.mentalhealth.org.uk/

The Mental Health Foundation works to improve the lives of those with mental health problems or learning difficulties.

www.mind.org.uk

The mental health charity. The Depression Alliance merged with Mind in August 2016 and provides information and support to those who are affected by depression via publications, supporter services and a network of self-help groups.

www.rethink.org

Since 1972 Rethink has been challenging attitudes and changing lives, helping people living with conditions like schizophrenia, bipolar disorder, personality disorders and more to recover a better quality of life.

www.stem4.org.uk

Teenage mental illness, including eating disorders, mental health, self harm and addiction.

www.together-uk.org/

Together is a national charity working alongside people with mental health issues on their journey towards independent and fulfilling lives.

https://www.youngminds.org.uk/

YoungMinds is the UK's leading charity committed to improving the emotional wellbeing and mental health of children and young people.